"Roberta Gregory is probably best known for her fiction. But now she turns her fertile imagination and inimitable drawing style to the world of 'based-on-a-true-story.' You're going to love what follows."

Kevin Boze, *The Virgin Project*

"A true Cat Lady in the nicest of terms; to know and love our feline friends for their whimsical and mystical personalities. Roberta's passion for sharing their tales reminds us all of the magic these furry bundles of joy bring to the lucky ones who get to share our lives with them. So much enjoyment for the price of a pooper scooper."

Joe Phillips, *Adventures of a Joe Boy!*

"I've been eagerly looking forward to this book ever since Roberta Gregory began working on it way back in 1 BCFB (Before Cats on Facebook). Every person has a story and every cat has at least a million. Who better to tell these tales than the talented Roberta? A legend and a pioneer in the comics business, Roberta is also a cat lover. In fact, I'm not entirely sure she isn't secretly a cat."

John Lustig, *Last Kiss*

"Honest, forthright and up-front, Roberta will give you the gift of both making you feel AND think."

Dave Mann, fanboy

True Cat Toons

By Roberta Gregory

Published by Roberta Gregory
2014

True Cat Toons

ISBN: 978-0-9619652-5-9

Published by: Roberta Gregory
PO Box 9599
Seattle WA 98109

roberta@drizzle.com

www.TrueCatToons.com

Intro by Roberta Gregory

I have been around cats all my life. One of my earliest childhood memories is a litter of grey and black kittens with cute names like Screamie Mimi, and Nosey Rosie. We had family cats, and when I moved out into the world, there always seemed to be a cat or three in my living situation. It took me a while to realize just how remarkable it is to share one's life with a little entity of a different species, so I began to pay more attention to the incredible little creatures. I believe everyone who coexists with a cat (or several) is an amateur Feline Behavior Field Researcher. As anyone who reads this book will clearly see.

My very first True Cat Toon is the last one in this book: the story "Bye Bye Muffy" published in 1999 in my comic book series *Naughty Bits*. My kitty had passed away recently and I realized that nobody had gotten a chance to know her, since she would often hide when anyone came to visit, and I felt the need to tell the world about her. Much to my surprise, the story earned me an Eisner Award nomination (the comic book industry's version of the Oscar). I illustrated stories about Pushkin, the next in line of my serial cats, but it wasn't until *Last Kiss* creator John Lustig organized the "Comics Biography Theater" project for Seattle's Bumbershoot Arts Festival, illustrating other folks' true stories, that it truly dawned on me that I wasn't the only one with cat tales to tell.

Fittingly, the first story, which I drew back in 2006, is told by Kevin Boze, also a Comics Biography artist, who went on to publish two volumes of *The Virgin Project,* his own comics based on people's true stories. From that point, I began to ask friends and colleagues (and sometimes perfect strangers) for their cat stories, and started a Facebook page, and the stories flooded in. Not only did these tales provide a fascinating look at feline behavior, observations from those who live with them, they also help preserve the memory of beloved companions who would otherwise be forgotten as their human friends passed on. I had other creative projects and a rather demanding day job, so it took me far too long to illustrate enough stories for this volume, while contributors waited patiently (I hope). So, I am happy to at last be able to bring some of these stories to readers.

YOUR CATS

These stories are presented roughly in the order in which they were drawn, the oldest first. Some of the contributors are professional writers, and many of these stories were easy to illustrate. Since comic captions cannot be too wordy, editing often had to be done, but I did my best to retain the unique language of the contributor. Some of the stories were narrated to me and I tried to capture the spirit of their words. Verna Black told her story of "The Cat Who Went To Alaska" in a wonderfully dry manner, and I hope I carried this into the story. Betty Gregory is my mom, who is 86 and I am happy to be able to publish her for the first time. I am also delighted that so many of these stories involve rescued cats, not to mention black cats, often the last to be adopted, if ever. "Kittikins" was a cat portrait for a colleague's Kickstarter campaign that I illustrated as a Cat Toon. Purrrzac makes her first appearance here, before she became my feline housemate and inspired my "Play Kitty" in the next section. And some of these contributors suggested that they had even more stories for me, so there will certainly be more Cat Toons to come.

Teaching Tool

Story: S.W. Conser

One day, I walked into the living room to see our cat, Zipperhead, conducting a class on the fine art of the "Mouse Pounce"... on a baby mouse! She was a semi-stray, so she held the mastery of hunting in high regard.

semi-circle of kittens

Whoa!

mommy...

She demonstrated from all sides—

I want my mommy...

When one of the young pupils lost interest and began to wander away...

My Mom came down the stairs and watched for a while until she noticed that a REAL MOUSE was involved...

EEP!

Rubber glove!

?

The mouse was quickly removed from the classroom.

You could almost read Zipper's mind--

Do I tell you how to raise YOUR children?

The next day, the lesson had resumed... but instead of a mouse, Zipper was using her plastic jingly ball.

HA!

tinkle

DETAIL

©2006 Roberta Gregory

3

CATLESS IN SEATTLE

story: Phyllis Solem

SHADOWBOXER 1992-2005	GINGERBAKER 2001-2006

A.K.A: Snookerpots " Shadow B.	A.K.A: Fluffy Baggins " Pussy Won-Kanobi

My husband Marc, being the frugal man that he is, "adopted" a tiny, black-and-white furball of a female kitten from one of the many free-roaming cats in his Capitol Hill neighborhood.

He set up her "nursery" and fed her canned milk from an eyedropper until she was old enough to eat dry solid food.

She liked to just sit in the shower stall and even took showers with Marc once in a while.

She didn't need catnip. Just a wadded-up wrapper from a Ricola cough drop would make her go crazy.

This was a few months before we got married. Marc knew I liked cats.

She was our bed pal and proved to be a good mouser.

About nine years after we moved to our house on Beacon Hill, Gingerbaker came into our lives. Marc heard him crying underneath some sticker bushes and decided to rescue him.

MEEW!

He was a sweet-faced little bundle of reddish-brown fur and he captured my heart.

Shadowboxer, who was 11 years old, was clearly jealous of our addition to the family.

Gingerbaker as a kitten also got the eye-dropper feeding and then he grew fat on dry food and water.

Purrr - Purrr - Purrr

We had to have Shadowboxer put to sleep when she was 13.

Bye, Mom...

Gingerbaker lived 5 years, and then suffered from a serious liver disease and passed away. It broke our hearts.

They filled in the gap when Marc was at work. Ginger would keep me company when I was on the computer.

When he was a little tyke, he liked to perch on top of the monitor. When he was bigger, he just sat to the left of the keyboard, content to be with me.

Life will not be the same without my kitties.

Roberta Gregory

Very truly catless in Seattle.

Who's There?

story: Bill Dodge

Most cats are happy to just leave a dead mouse on the doorstep...

(Repeat over and over and over and OVER and OVER..)

...NOT MIDNIGHT!

PURRRZAC...
The Therapy Cat!

Story: Bruce Taylor

Mee?

When I acquired the little kitten from a stranger in the Animal Shelter parking lot, I had no idea what a remarkable cat she'd grow into.

She was a tiny kitten covered with (highly contagious) ringworm, but she became a beautiful, long-haired adult cat who resembles a Maine Coon, or Norwegian Forest Cat.

I am a retired mental health worker from a large Seattle hospital.. so, I named her "Purrrzac".. as in a feline version of Prozac, because cats are a natural "upper."

Om..

Sometimes I see hypnotherapy clients in my home. and Purrrzac seems to know when someone needs comforting, or a bit of feline therapy. She comes up to them and purrs, and lends her support.

All the clients she has "chosen" seem to be the ones who appreciate cats.

I was undergoing some therapy of my own, which I found very beneficial, and Purrrzac seemed to quickly pick up on my "mellower vibes" because since then. she spends much more time near me, as if enjoying my energy.

She is truly a remarkable cat..

..And THEN sometimes she poops on the carpet!

??! ?? !!!

Roberta Gregory

--- CATS!! Oh. well.. Ya still gotta love 'em!

Othello's Story

story: Elizabeth Pankey

Roger knew Othello would be growing bigger with our care.

Othello was adopted from the Humane Society. Roger named him after the Black Moor of Shakespeare's play because this cat was all black except for a tiny tuft of white on his chest.

He did grow bigger and more muscular. Othello loved sitting, or should I say, lounging on our laps. He loved being outside when we were outside.

After many, many years of good health, he started to succumb to old cat troubles. During the last two years of his life, Othello welcomed a very skinny little black cat into our yard.

Since Othello started to get picky about what food he'd eat, we gave the little black cat Othello's leftovers.

The little one stayed around more and more. I decided to name him "Little Black Gin" because he would just appear and then disappear.

Gin would stay close to Othello when Othello went outside. They didn't fight. On sunny days they'd lounge together on the back lawn or back deck.

Gin would follow Othello around to make sure he was okay.

Othello felt safe in the backyard with Gin there to chase the other cats away. Othello couldn't fight his own battles anymore.

When Othello's kidneys began to fail and he let us know it was time to say goodbye, we had to have the vet put our dear friend into his eternal sleep. It was the hardest decision we have ever made.

Our other cats had died without our aid. One night, our black cat Sebastian died of old age in our backyard. Little Quincy, a gray shorthair, died after being hit by a car. He was too adventurous for his own good.

We mourned Sebastian's passing more than Quincy, but the worst pain is saying goodbye at the clinic. The pain is still in our hearts whenever we remember that moment.

Othello Angel Picture: Elizabeth Pankey

Little Black Gin misses Othello, too. But, Gin is now our attentive pet. He comes in for breakfast and dinner. He loves lots of petting and rubbing of his cheeks and under his chin.

He is not a lap cat and never learned to play, but he is a mouser.

Gin senses when I'm not able to pet him anymore, and asks to go back outside. There is still plenty of independent, feral cat in Gin.

But then, all cats act independent though they depend on us for scheduled feeding and attention.

We've never shared our lives with any dumb animals. Cats are intelligent creatures with good senses.

© 2010 Art. Roberta Gregory

Some can be bitches, but that is why we've only housed male cats!

9

SNEAKERS
story: Deborah Fredericks

Can't touch that!

whisk!

She came from a shelter but we think she was a barn cat before that. She needs people to keep their distance, and hates to be held —

She likes to sit in my office while I'm writing — just watching, no touchie.

But, one day I suddenly had a cat on my desk.

I gently put her down...

But, then she jumped onto my lap! She'd never done that before.

Sneakers stepped on my headphone cord and pulled them off my ears.

Only then did I realize my daughter Cora was crying in the back yard. Sneakers knew she was in trouble and came to get me.

Together we comforted Cora and bandaged her scraped knee.

Sneakers saved the day!

The Cat Who Thought He Could Bark

Story: Lenora Rain-Lee Good

We expected him to enjoy his laps and naps during the day, but at night he was adamant in his demands to stay outdoors.

Once upon a time, not so very long ago, we were acquired by a large, twenty-six pound, red-orange cat. There was no way we could have known about our new owner's identity crisis.

My husband and I named him "O.C." for Outside Cat.

Apparently, this was acceptable, as he did now and then answer to it.

Our Cat was a very friendly, laid-back, short-haired cat who not only inspired vocabulary building and dictionary use, but also manifested a strange sort of schizophrenia.

Sonja and Aaron, aged 13 and 9, soon entered into a contest to see who could come up with the best "O.C." names that lasted for several months.

Okay Cat, when not acting as a dictionary cat, thought he was a dog!

Though he would occasionally respond to his name, he would almost always come running if we whistled.

Orange Cat spent most of the day inside, sleeping on a lap if he could find one, or on whoever's bed was soaking up the sun's warmth.

The humongous Ocular Cat did sleep like a cat, that is, all day. His naps were interrupted only by demands from his stomach and the occasional visitor.

11

At night, Oddball Cat would go outside and run with the dogs.

If the Obdurate Cat was late for the nightly gathering, the little barking fur ball would come to our front door and bark and whine until he went outside.

There was one Doberman, two German Shepherds, four medium-sized mongrels and a little barking "fur ball" (I think it was a Peekapoo) that Obsolete Cat counted as his friends.

The pack would then make the rounds of the neighborhood until their people were making breakfast the next morning.

The fur ball often came to the house during the day. Anytime he was lonely, he'd come bark for the Oblivious Cat to come play. "Fur Ball" was a polite little dog who never tried to come into the house.

He would just softly bark for his friend while leaning as far through the open door as he could.

Our brave and ferocious Occidental Cat feared nothing. He would stand his ground and take no guff from man nor child, nor dog.

Many times I would go outside to find the car surrounded by his strange mixture of doggy friends, with the Official Cat sitting on the hood like a judge presiding over his court.

One day, after keeping the neighborhood safe all night with his pack of obviously confused pooches, our Opinionated Cat came into his home expecting praise from his people for a job well-done, food from his dish and peace for his naps.

Instead, he was met at the door by a tiny, gray and white kitten named Rambo.

All twenty-six pounds of the Orbital Cat jumped straight up. He bounced from wall to wall gaining altitude until he was high enough to land on top of the dining room hutch.

Rambo tried to jump for his new friend; he meowed; he purred.

The Oxymoronic Cat cowered; he quaked; he made pitiful noises; he hissed at all who came near.

Rambo wanted to play; our Onerous Cat wanted to go outside but could not get past the ferocious kitten.

Somehow, the Owl-eyed Cat called his buddies, for soon after this started, the barking for ball came to the door.

When Rambo saw the dog — he spit and ran, allowing our Oversized Cat to escape to the outdoors where he would be protected by his pack of dogs.

Eventually, the Orderly Cat came to be friendly to Rambo. When Rambo had been at the house about five weeks...

...I walked into a room to see our Omega Cat sprawled on his back with his eyes closed and his purr motor going full bore and baby Rambo trying his best to get milk from a neutered tom's teat.

Together, the Omnipotent Cat and Rambo prowled the fields around our neighborhood for mice and shrews, but Rambo knew there was a basic difference between cats and dogs.

He never ran with the pack and he never learned to bark.
🐾   THE END   🐾

Tommy Tales:
A chapter in the ongoing saga of "CATS HAPPEN"
story: Susan Williams

I've never had to actively search for a cat - they've always found ME!

It started with my first apartment back in college days - 1971. The previous renter was going to travel in her VW van...

She figured it would be difficult to take her cat along.

So, that's how I got a cat (Sarah) along with the apartment!

Shag carpet

Unbeknownst to us, Sarah was pregnant. That was how Pumpkin (a tortoise shell kitty born in October) appeared on the scene.

Sarah disappeared under mysterious circumstances when she was 12.

SAN FRAN

Pumpkin wandered off shortly before her 16th birthday - never to be seen again.

Jasmine, the most special kitty in my life, was a "child of a broken home." When a relationship unexpectedly ended, I got custody of the "kid."

silver tabby

Hee-eere's TOMMY!
When I lived in a Spanish-style duplex, the folks in the back had 2 cats that came to them:

DANNY, a long-haired orange tabby, and TOMMY, a black short-hair with a notch in his left ear.

I took care of "the boys in the back" when their folks were out of town.

NO?

I TOLD you this wouldn't work.

My neighbors decided to move to Hawaii, where they had relatives, but they weren't sure what to do with the cats. Due to strict rules about bringing animals into Hawaii, they couldn't take them.

Meanwhile, Jasmine lived a long life and at the age of 21, developed kidney failure.

cat heaven

It was time for the "last trip" to the vet's office...

When I returned home, I felt the need to do some sort of ritual.

I put on a tape of Native American flute music, and lit white sage in an abalone shell and walked throughout the house.

The french doors leading out into the back yard were open. Just as the last musical notes faded away and the last wisps of sage smoke drifted upward...

You have a... VACANCY?

...TOMMY poked his head inside the door!

I thought to myself...

OH, NO...not THAT cat!

And that's how — Tommy the Terrible came to live with me!

Tommy was very territorial and wanted to be King of the Household.

This was fine with Danny- he preferred to be outside.

The landlord needed to do major renovations, so I had to move. I bought a mobile home, and Tommy came with me, and learned to be an indoor kitty.

Bye, pal-

There was no way Danny could be an inside cat. He stayed with some folks down the street in our old neighborhood.

Tommy was actually a pretty sweet cat, but didn't like to be picked up or held. He was a bit shy around strangers, but liked the elderly lady across the street and would greet Dotti whenever she came to visit.

He had quite a kitty vocabulary and I learned some of his vocalizations. He talked to himself quite a bit, including a worried-sounding mumbling. There was a distinctive sound he made when he wanted to be fed.

15

And then there was his "Territorial Yowl," really quite amusing given the circumstances..

Even though the pets in the "park" are supposed to be indoors-only, some do get out occasionally. Tommy would get visitors at the screen door and sliding door. This didn't prompt too much reaction.

DANGER!

However, there is Shadow, a gray tomcat who is a Park Cat - not really a stray, but doesn't belong to anyone, though a few folks put food out for him.

When Shadow appeared at the sliding door, Tommy would make some small sounds -- almost submissive.

TOM CAT
Neutered

But, after Shadow left, (often with "pee mail" behind) Tommy would get brave and start a rather shattering yowl and run to all the windows and doors declaring his territory.

A few months ago, it was obvious Tommy didn't feel well. I took him to the vet - it turned out he was extremely anemic. His blood tests didn't indicate kidney damage, the usual suspect.

We tried a variety of treatments for him ...

But, Tommy didn't want to eat, though he'd drink water. It was like he had his own idea what he wanted, so I went into "Kitty hospice" mode--

.. keeping him as comfortable as possible. It was a swift decline. His initial vet visit was on a Friday. By the next Friday, it was time to say goodbye.

The Saga Continues -
Three and a half weeks after saying goodbye to Tommy, I was mowing the little lawn in front of my mobile home, when...

HEY! Do you know who belongs to this cat?

It was apparently dumped here. Given the home foreclosures, there's a lot of that these days.

And thus begins the adventures with -- "Stumpy Luke", a young, neutered-male Mainly Manx with a touch of Siamese --

Blue, slightly crossed eyes

But, that's another story..

16

SHOWBIZ Kitties

Out of a litter of five, we picked two.

Story: Michael Paul ©'10

One chose Thom...

We went home with the three!

The kittens were foster cared by our friend... ---CINDY.

Love... exciting and MEW!

Take us home --we've been expecting --MEW!

In keeping with their show-biz heritage, we named them after characters on **FRIENDS.**

How YOU doin'?

"Handle" is my middle name!

Purrrrr...

JOEY

GUNTHER

CHANDLER

GUNTHER (aka Schmo) was the first of the kittens to purr. He purrs the loudest and the longest...

Purrrrrr rrrrrrr rrrrr...

...(especially if he gets his left fang/tooth rubbed!)

CHANDLER (aka Chonzi Bonz) loves to head butt..

...HARD! Concussions are a concern for everybody!

JOEY (nicknamed Cry Baby by Cindy) has a large and often insistent vocabulary...

Art ©'10 Roberta Gregory

He demands that Thom lie down so all 15 pounds of him can climb on his chest, lick his face and then go to sleep.

17

This is the story of the Twin Black Demons of Chaos—

AZATHOTH and YOG-SOTOTH

written by Justine Graykin

It began last summer, when the 12-year old daughter of the farmers we buy our milk from said

"Isn't he ADORABLE? Our cat had four of them and they need homes—"

I admired the kitten. But I already had 5 cats.

The LAST thing I needed was 2 more mouths to feed. Plus, the vet bills, stress of integrating them into the household— no, no, I could not bear the thought. the unspeakable horror of it!

But, Grace was a good salesperson—

"Here— HOLD HIM!"

That's when I saw.. those FEET! Those marvelous feet. Double paws front and back. Then he looked up at me and opened his mouth --

"ME!"

The demon sultan had spoken. What else was there to say?

It turned out he had a brother, also black, also with the same huge double feet.

Kittens are always better in pairs; they keep each other company.

On the one hand, they play with each other and aren't bored. Bored kittens are a disaster looking for a venue.

On the other hand, if they are evil demons, they are the forces of chaos personified--
--times two.

After trying on an assortment of ill-fitting appellations, I returned from Readercon with the perfect names for them: Azathoth and Yog-Sothoth

Which any reader of Lovecraft will know is just asking for trouble.

As soon as they were old enough to climb they joined the Society for Removing Things from On Top of Other Things.

Their specialty was testing the law of gravity by launching small objects off tables and counters.

Pencils, papers, napkins, CDs, silverware — If they could budge it, they could knock it to the floor.

I once observed Yog-Sothoth gleefully swat a small glass dish off the table and watch it smash on the floor with decided satisfaction.

That being accomplished, he gave his swatting apparatus a few proud licks, and moved on to the spoon.

He was displeased when I interrupted him in his task with unreasonable force --

Azathoth, the Demon Sultan, preferred observing his realm from the noble height provided by a human servant's shoulder.

The convenience of the human was irrelevant.

Should his loud commands of "ME!" not be heeded in a timely manner, he would enforce his rule by using those seven-clawed feet to scale the human as if it were a tree.

A determined kitten has little difficulty climbing up a person's trousers with the aid of 28 needle-sharp grappling hooks...

..by the time he has reached the belt-line, a sensible human surrenders and does as he has been commanded to do.

My elder son (14) is a fan of origami, and brought home an assortment of folded novelties - flying boxes, cranes, stellated isohedrons - that sort of thing. What perfect toys!

Or, rather... prey.

A jumping frog proved to be a favorite. Removed from the table by the usual method -

They took turns, batting the helpless thing around.

Then one would take it in his mouth and growl menacingly, bearing its prey off down the stairs into the basement, to unimaginable tortures.

It was difficult at first to distinguish who was who since they were both coal-black with identical pedal weaponry.

Azathoth was smaller. Yog-Sothoth developed a patch of white on his chest.

Their behaviour was slightly different, too.

AZI

YOG

Dignified

Clingy and demanding

Yog favored my younger son, Alec (11) while Azi has decided I am the favored servant...

...and still hauls himself up by means of my clothing if I don't respond to his demands to be picked up.

The other cats adjusted to the demons with difficulty. At first, they were all incredulous that I should bring these obnoxious twin menaces into our settled home.

There were unpleasant disagreements, but slowly things sorted themselves out.

Fagen, who'd previously been the benevolent ruler of my shoulder, got terribly depressed.

I had to carry him around and fuss over him for weeks to assure him that he hadn't been rejected.

This meant I had a cat perched on me nearly all the time. I felt like a new mother again, having to do everything with one hand while holding the baby with the other.

Mommy..

Whenever Azi was amusing himself by tormenting his paper frog I was obliged to give quality time to Fagen.

PLUS the liberal distribution of petting, brushing and affection to the rest of the tribe, to keep them from getting their little pink noses out of joint--

Hmph..

The dogs figured it out quickly. Maybe they could get the other cats to run away if they rushed at them - (all a game, of course)-

!

But, the demons had no intention of letting mere dogs intimidate them.---

Fritz was baffled when he came rushing at Yog, barking furiously, only to find--

But- But - You're supposed to run AWAY when I do that..

Go boil your head, canine scum!

Our other dog, Elke, always a bit of an obsequious toady, realized that these were the true rulers of the house. and she'd better make nice.

Heh..

So, she began doing the submissive thing, rolling on her back before them, and the "Wanna Play" thing crouching and wagging her tail.

This amused the demons.

After a few of these performances, they began to play with Elke.

21

Elke would poke her muzzle as close to the demon as she could, then duck back when the demon swatted a massive mitt at her.

The demon would roll on his back and wave his paws enticingly. Elke would again crouch, thrust, parry, back and forth, testing her reflexes against those of the dark lord.

She has only been nailed a couple of times.

It has been several months since the Twin Black Demons of Chaos have come among us. We have accepted our fate.

The other cats have realized the presence of the newcomers doesn't interfere with the regular serving of meals, so it's all right.

Becker, an amiable monster of 16-odd pounds, has even taken to playing with them from time to time — the typical cat thing of racing from room to room, chasing each other —

—although Becker is a bit clumsy and has an unfortunate tendency to crash into things.

The two demons also have decided that they like the practice of going on walks.

When I summon "the canines" for daily "walkies," Azi and Yog come running. We make an interesting troupe —

—myself, my younger son, Alec, two dogs, a shih-tzu (who doesn't really count as a dog)—

— and two black kittens, (now nearly adult-sized) all puttering along at various paces, more or less keeping up with one another.

And now I am very sure, very, very sure I will not get any more kittens. This is enough. Honestly. This time I mean it.

Besides, the Demon Sultan may not approve. And woe betide us if we incur his wrath.

KITTIKINS *in action*

by Korcaigne Hale

©13 Roberta Gregory

THE END

Singer, the Therapy Cat

Story: Linda Jean Shepherd

Science Stuff...

...to restore internal rotation to my shoulder joint. This involves lying on my right side extending my arm out to the side at shoulder level ....

Last September I began physical therapy to return range of motion to my shoulder. Before getting out of bed, I do a stretching exercise....

...then bending at the elbow and pressing down on my wrist and forearm. The idea is to have my palm flat on the mattress, with fingers pointing to my navel.

Over the past month, my Maine Coon Cat, Singer, has been coming by to help me. She knows when I'm waking...

She trots upstairs, jumps on the bed, purring, and comes over to me, her pupils dilated.

..even if she's downstairs on the back of the couch, warming herself over the baseboard heater which comes on at 6:30 am.

She puts her front paws on my forearm to exert just the right amount of pressure to push my arm to the mattress.

She knows exactly where to put her paws, despite the big fluffy comforter covering me.

Of course, I give her a nice petting after our therapy session.

Roberta Gregory

She's been gradually increasing the pressure, so now most of her body is on my forearm.

I often kiss her on her head between her ears; the other morning she lick-kissed my cheek before starting our therapy.

MEWNIN'S STORY
BY: Lori Frostad

Our cat Mewnin has been unconventional from the start. We didn't pick her — -- SHE picked us!

Her old owners nicknamed her "Ivy" because, if she liked you, she'd climb your leg like a pesky barbed vine.

The very day she climbed up our legs, we decided to bring her home.

She was very easygoing. My daughter Emma was able to dress her in dolls' clothes. Mewnin now has quite the extensive cat wardrobe.

This luxurious feline is also pampered with her very own "spa day" complete with tail-softening treatments and relaxing Herb Alpert Tijuana Brass music.

She has only caught one bird in her life. Her other hunting feats include a rubber snake, an earplug and a Nerf dart.

Though a docile soul, she has collected some enemies over the years. They engage in "Kitten Karaoke" – Mewnin usually wins!

Because Mewnin was the littlest of the bunch, she learned at an early age how to self-soothe. She curls into a tortoiseshell ball and nurses the tip of her tail.

Now bleached light brown!

If you were to meet her you would be greeted by a bump against your leg and a swoosh of her Swiffer tail. She'll cheer you up when you are sick: a constant friend on your bed.

Even though she can be a handful at times, we love her dearly and wouldn't trade her for anyone!

25

THE CAT'S MEOW!

STORY:
KEITH BOE

Mads Maks is a very laid-back Ragdoll cat.

Tredjekatten is a little stinker!

Even when my Murphy bed is put away, Tredjekatten treats it like it's his.

He loves to shred paper and cardboard, and to knock objects onto the floor.

LOOK OUT BELOW!

To keep him entertained, I bought one of those "Cats Meow" toys.

on-off button

"MOOSE TAIL" whips around underneath fabric...

For awhile, at least, everything was fine...

26

Then I noticed one day it had been turned on. And I hadn't done it!

I finally caught Tredge doing it by himself. He used his right back paw. (I use my right foot.)

Looks like he's starting a motorcycle.

Once it's on, he doesn't seem to play with it. It would be nice if he'd turn it OFF, too!

C batteries are NOT cheap!

One day I had a friend visit who insists dogs are "better" than cats. Of course, I always stand up for cats.

So, to demonstrate, I told Tredge to turn on the "Cats Meow." He turned it on... AND off.. TWICE!

Score one MORE for the CATS!

The Attack of the UNSTOPPABLE
TOILET SHARK
story: Seanan McGuire

Over the past week my house has developed two new bathroom-based rules:

FIRST! Even if you've just dropped a tissue into the water- FLUSH!*

* I don't CARE if it wastes water!

SECOND! Close the LID! Not the seat, the LID! WHY...?

..Because Alice, like so many Maine Coons, likes to play with water. And the TOILET...? FULL of WATER!

Once your nasty tissue has been in the water, I don't particularly want the cat to bring it to me, thanks!

Last night when I got home from work I performed the standard checks: Are both cats present? Breathing? Have they broken anything large and/or visible...?

After confirming: YES, YES and NO, I went about my business.

Alice wandered off to do kitten things - which usually end with a loud CRASH! and a startled-looking puffball racing back to the bedroom— no big deal!

After unpacking bags, scanning some art cards and eating dinner, I proceeded to the bathroom. The toilet lid was down.

I repeat, DOWN, indicating safety... I began to sit...

The toilet said, inquisitively...

Having seen approximately 800 Hours' worth of horror cinema in my lifetime, I was fully dressed in less than five seconds and standing in the bathtub. I looked into the toilet bowl...

Alice, balled calmly in the bottom of it, looked back at me...

Meet my kitten:
THE TOILET SHARK!

I got her to leave the toilet by putting a few inches of water in the tub. She happily submerged several of her feather toys and went off to coax Lily in...

Lily being, I don't know, AN ACTUAL CAT, was having none of it.

Alice got her comeuppance later when her aquatic adventures required her to get a good brushing.

Horror movies of the 1980s taught me to check toilets first because they might contain monsters. It took years to break this habit, thinking it was just a foolish fear.

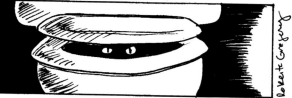

In conclusion, when you come over to my place, look down before you pee.
...YOU MIGHT BE SORRY IF YOU DON'T!

29

JUNIOR
story: Betty Gregory

Junior lived across our cul-de-sac driveway. He was a cute, feisty little black cat.

His owners' upstairs bedroom had a sliding door that they kept ajar and a balcony Junior climbed on to by way of the tree growing next to it.

One day his family moved a short distance away. Junior preferred his old neighborhood and would come back, walking over a culvert and a rugged half mile along San Juan Creek.

His owner, Judy, who worked at a nearby marina, would come during her lunch hour to look for him and bring him home. But Junior was back the next day.

One evening I heard him at our upstairs window, clinging to the screen. He'd tried to get in like he'd done at his old home but we had no balcony.

And then Judy stopped by. She said it had been a year now and her husband was fed up with Junior's early morning persistence to be let out. She would have to give up.

©2013 R. Gregory

She knew we would look after him. I felt bad for her but you couldn't help but fall in love with the little guy.

GRATITUDE:
The Fruit Cat Story

As told by Karen Geer

Twenty years ago, I lived in a ramshackle Victorian affectionately called Toad Hall. A couple doors up the street was a crazy cat lady.

She fed a vast colony of feral cats and never tried to neuter them.

This really didn't bother me much until spring rolled around and a mother cat would give birth to kittens in the garden shed or under the house.

Every year I'd take the kittens to the ASPCA - and the next year... MORE kittens!

After many years, I had finally had enough, and vowed to not get involved in the feline misery. As Buddha said: "All life is sorrowful."

One spring, a litter of four kittens arrived, and the first I spied of them was the tiniest of the bunch strutting across the parking lot behind the house like he owned it.

As much as I enjoyed watching the brood with the funny little runt gambol about, I held firm: Do not get involved.

Then one night, I pulled into the parking lot. Three of the kittens scattered, but the runt sat alone, unable to move because an eye infection had glued his eyes shut.

He sat there mewling pathetically for the others. I knew he would not survive the night.

I sighed deeply and grabbed him by the scruff and took him inside.

All life may be Sorrow, but SOMETIMES there's Sh*t you can actually DO something about!

As I held him to my chest, he purred mightily. That's how Moses came into my life.

A year and a half later, I was making the bed when a yellow zucchini rolled out of the sheets. My brain joked:

WHAT did you get UP to last night?

A close inspection revealed cat teeth marks all over it. I threw it away and thought little of it.

A couple of weeks later, I woke up and my hand came down on something wet and unpleasant. Every pet owner has experienced this. But, when I checked, I found... ORANGE GOO!

OKAY... I KNOW my cat is WEIRD-- But--?

It was a half-eaten persimmon. I had intended to use it as part of a Thanksgiving Centerpiece.

My next day off, I was treated to the sight of Moses carrying an apple in his teeth!

He would carefully pick it up, walk a few paces, put it down, then repeat.

This was a huge Granny Smith bigger than his head. The distance from the kitchen is a good fifty feet.

An impressive stretch for a cat imitating a famous Magritte painting.

I finally realized that, since Toad Hall was shockingly void of mice, my blue-gray darling...

...was bringing the next best (though vastly heavier) thing!

I praised him loudly and pretended to eat the tooth-marked apple, and did my best to hide the fact that I was tossing it.

I think I even tucked it in my work bag so there'd be no evidence.

Another week passed, and then I woke to something that left the apple carry in the dust. Moses was dragging a banana across the floor.

This time, I picked up both banana and cat. Sitting in bed with Moses beside me, I peeled the banana and, finding it free of teethmarks, ate it, making lots of "yummy" sounds.

He never did it again.

Why would a cat show such dogged (sorry!) determination? I believe it was gratitude for saving his life. In return for this small act--

I got a zucchini, a persimmon, an apple, a banana and the company of the funniest, cuddliest, biggest personality I have ever known on four feet.

Moses is 19 and a half now, and diabetic, and spends most days sleeping on the couch. He will leave me in the not-too-distant future. But, I am grateful beyond measure for each day I get with my little man.

Theologians, philosophers and scientists might argue if a dog can go to heaven or a cat can feel love and gratitude.

Let them argue—
I have my answer!

33

SING-ALONG

story: James Langdell

Sing Lee was my family's seal-point Siamese cat. Her son was Dunkle.

When our dishwasher was running, they would happily sit together on it, enjoying the warm surface and mechanical purring.

From the cats' perspective, my father called it "The Big Mama."

On a number of occasions, Sing Lee would play the piano in the living room. She jumped on to the keyboard ...

.. walked to the far left end and then plopped her body down, sounding and sustaining a cluster of low bass strings.

When the sound faded out, she raised her body up and plopped back down on the strings— setting them rumbling again.

Dunkle never seems to have caught on.

34

MOLLY the HELPFUL
story: Barbara Pett

Molly doesn't like having her nails clipped.

Molly does like to help me in the kitchen. So, we compromise by letting her sit on top of the fridge.

I used to keep the clippers in a basket on top of the fridge, until the day I heard a rustling...

...and saw Molly with the clippers in her mouth, about to drop them down the back of the fridge.

MOLLY!

Now, I keep the clippers in a drawer. After she has had her nails clipped (and given a treat) Molly will look for them....

She has stolen them a few times when I've forgotten to put them away.

Just helping you clean up, Mom..

INKWELL by Laura Gjovaag

I'm a reporter at a newspaper in a small Eastern Washington city.

It was a cold January Monday in 2012. There was leftover snow in our parking lot.

I was at my desk when I heard one of the ad gals saying something about how cute the cat was.

Sitting on the counter was the cutest little black kitten with four muddy paws.

I came over and touched its head. It purred loudly. My fingers were sticky with motor oil.

Turns out the little beast had just been found in the wheel well of a car about to drive off.

A female customer had spotted it and stopped the car just in time. The couple brought it in.

The man whose car the kitten had been found in wanted nothing to do with it and was hoping to get on with his errands.

The kitten had probably been in the car engine for a bit and come from somewhere else in town...

There was no place near our building it could have gotten the muddy paws. Someone ran to the press room for a towel, and we wiped the kitten off.

Somehow I was talked into taking the kitten to a vet. We put it into a box...

I drove to the vet's office with the little kitten purring so loudly that it drowned out the road noises.

I found out the kitten was a "he", 3 or 4 months old, well·fed, in good health and very friendly. He needed a bath and an exam.

I agreed to take him home while we looked for his owner.

I went back to finish the story I was working on, and then picked up the now-clean kitten.

We dubbed him "Inkwell," from when the oil dripped off his fur, and the fact that he was found at a newspaper office.

I left Inkwell at home with my confused and concerned hubby, while I took off to get pictures of a basketball game.

We ran an ad in the paper about the cat, but nobody stepped forward to claim him.

Two days later, Inkwell got sick, throwing up food. He had bouts of getting better, then would get very sick again, but he pulled through.

He was diagnosed with Feline Herpes, fairly common in strays.

The fellow who had brought him into the office came back with some cat food, treats and toys—

—to say "Thank you" for helping to rescue the kitten.

Inkwell has now been with us for over a year, and every once in a while, I still pick him up and say —

"Wow! We have a Cat!"

The Cat who went to ALASKA

BY: Verna Black

Perlina was named after an older lady from Rhodes I used to take care of.

She loved to sit in my kitchen window, enjoying the view from three floors up.

One day I heard her screech. She ran from the kitchen and under the bed.

An orange tabby tomcat had somehow climbed all the way up to the window.

He stayed there all afternoon and peed all over the window. I had just washed that window.

Perlina stayed under the bed.

When I came back from shopping, I saw that he'd finally gotten down from the window and was gone.

Perlina came out from under the bed, but she never sat in that window again.

One day, the tomcat got into the van of some neighbors who moved to Portland.

But they brought him back.

A month later, he got into the van of some neighbors who were moving to Anchorage.

And he never returned.

COOPER BLACK

by: URSULA MURRAY HUSTED

I had gone through an awful breakup in 2007, and my mentor, Frenchy Lunning, decided I needed a cat!

We went to the humane society's cat colony and I sat on the floor.

All the cats ignored me, and I felt worse than before. I had been rejected by everyone, and now even the cats didn't want me!.

When I stood to go, two little yellow eyes peered out of my shoulder bag. They seemed to say:

Get me OUT of here!

When I went to fill out paperwork they told me he had been returned to the shelter three times and I was pretty much his last chance.

I got my first good look at him as he explored my apartment. He had dull, patchy black fur and was painfully scrawny, with a long tail and fat feet.

I named him "Cooper Black" after the heavily serifed typeface.

After a few months of good food he bulked out and grew a glossy new coat. I've never known such an amiable and kind soul.

When I'm unhappy, he puts his little paws on my face and sleeps in the crook of my arm. He loves when I draw, and sits in my lap for hours.

He even behaves beautifully on car and plane trips, and always purrs for the TSA agents, who insist on patting him down for tiny cat weapons.

Coop is quite simply the best cat in the world, and has been so ever since the day he picked me out.

40

Sedro-Wooley

Story: Ann Bellov

I live on Whidbey Island. I once had a cat named Sedro Wooley.

But, one day when I was out of town, Sedro Wooley disappeared.

At the time, Coyotes were all over the place, and cats were disappearing like mad.

So, after a few days and nights of looking and calling for him, I was in bed, crying myself to sleep, listening to the coyotes howl...

.. and I felt four very distinct small footsteps walk over me just like he used to do at night to sleep on my chest.

It was at that point that I knew he was gone.

41

My Best Friend

Story: Candace Behuniak

Art: Roberta Gregory

Having a special relationship with another is a vital part of the human experience. Friendship and love is a driving force. I have a bond of mutual respect and unconditional love with my housemate—a relationship so rare and magical, death won't break its spell.

My studio

My studio partner and I are lifelong companions living in an artistic environment; an animation studio. Its full of specialized books, dictionaries, hundreds of VHS and DVD's, landscape paintings, grey marbled desk with two monitors and two corporate swivel chairs...

.. as well as a bed, chair and large TV. Several concept art illustrations decorate the walls and stuffed Disney characters are poised at the keyboard.

If you haven't figured it out by now, my best friend has long, white whiskers, four paws and a tail—my cat Tommy Boy. He's a highly intelligent, 18-pound tabby with large emerald green eyes and a beautiful coat with striped jungle cat markings. He lives at the 9th floor Belltown studio.

My met pet seems to take living there matter-of-factly, although I can tell he feels special. Like all cats, Tommy possesses a curious nature, always seeking a new place to explore. He nestles into one of the safehouses I created for him with chairs and blankets.

Tommy watches me from his wooden perch while I write, creating a calming influence for me while I work. Although independent in nature, Tommy Boy, upon seeing a manuscript, or screenplay, lies on it. I think he knows its value and takes pride in guarding its valuable contents.

Our studio apartment affords a coveted Puget Sound view of sailboats, cruise ships and seagulls. Tommy sits at his window perch, tail rigid, ears up and alert. Although he gets peace from window watching, curled up at his overlook for hours, he's actually a 'fraidy cat, especially when the fire alarm goes off. He knows the moment he hears the **TIC·TIC·TIC·TIC** that doom is imminent. He races under the bed before the ticking is replaced with the deafening **UUUARN, UUUARN, UARN!**

Although he doesn't care for "people food" we have a special thing at breakfast time. The minute Tommy hears me getting a cereal box out of the cupboard, he comes running into the kitchen, jumps up onto a high stool and watches me pour it into the bowl. He quickly follows me into the living room to dine. Tommy loves Heart Smart Cereal milk. While Tommy is lapping the milk on one side of the bowl, I'm eating on the other side. (With a spoon, of course!)

Tommy loves our communal bathroom. Each of us has our own "potty box;" mine, the traditional white ceramic throne, and his an upgraded covered condo-style litter box. He flops down on the fluffy rug at my feet while I take a recess in the loo, looking up at me adoringly.

Tommy has an affinity for people who have experienced loss. My relationships have been complicated and painful. When I am heartbroken, sick, or injured, Tommy comes to my rescue, tending to my needs, gently placing one of his paws on my cheek, staring at me with loving eyes or holding my hand with a paw.

He frequently visits our neighbor, waiting until both our apartment doors are open. Tommy began to frequent her home more often after the recent passing of her companion Houdini. His friendship made a difference throughout her ordeal.

There was also an old shuffle couple who lived down the hall. Occasionally, when my door was open, Tommy ran out to the woman, skillfully moving back and forth at her feet, careful not to knock her down. She bent down slowly and petted him, saying, "Tommy Boy is part of our family, as well." In reply, Tommy would purr thunderously.

Albert Schweitzer said it best: "You can't own a cat. The best you can do is be partners."

If everyone was able to give unconditional love like MY best friend, the world would be a better place. I'm lucky he shares his life with me and I hope to spend a long time with him. Unlike humans who criticize and belittle each other, we have a bond of mutual admiration, respect and unconditional love – one which death will not break. It is better to have loved and lost than never to have loved at all. If we can be inspired by Tommy, we'll find the courage to risk the pain that comes when you are willing to trust and love.

LOOK... LOOK!
STORY BY: Kathryn Cramer

My 5-year old son Peter had an African Albino Clawed frog that lived in an aquarium in his room.

Belinda came to us from a rare book dealer who had too many cats.

COO·OL!

My step-son Geoff is a musician. One night he came home from a gig in the wee hours and came across Belinda—

?

She was urgently trying to get him to go into the kitchen, almost as if she was saying:

Come HERE— you'll see— Just LOOK-- Go IN there—

The frog had escaped its aquarium and was in need of rescue. It was covered in lint, cat hairs, dust, and anything else a damp amphibian might collect as it wandered about.

Roberta Gregory

Told you...

MY CATS

The stories in this section are presented in reverse order, the newest first; Roo is the current kitty in my life. I illustrated other stories about Pushkin and Purrrzac, but since they are a bit repetitive I will probably put them on the website or in a future volume. And last but not least is my first story, "Bye Bye Muffy.". I imagine someone on the Eisner Awards Nomination panel must have had to say goodbye to a four footed friend at the time these were compiled. As the saying goes, the more personal our stories, the more universal they become. The better I get to know the cats who share my life, the more I am convinced that there is so much these little critters want to tell us. Although they are always considered to be independent animals, they rely so heavily upon us humans for their well-being and security. When one stops to think about it, it is truly remarkable to share one's life so intimately with another species. It is in this spirit that I hope my own stories will be perceived.

ROO TUNE

How this wonderful little guy came into our lives--

By Roberta Gregory

Bruce Just LOves his Subaru (Built in 1982)--

RED!

The problem with an older car? Sometimes you won't get too far!

when finding parts starts getting hard/Time to find a wrecking yard!

So, he and Roberta drove over the Pass/ All the way to Kittitas'!

SEATTLE

ELLENSBURG

KITTITAS

Mount Rainier

Roberta's 1993 Subie

rhymes with PASS

TO YAKIMA

(That's Ellensburg, plus a little more)/ Though Roberta finds car parts a big, fat BORE!

When Bruce went in to see what they got/ Roberta sat out in the parking lot...

'Cause the day was bright, and the sky was pretty /and wandering around was a black & white kitty!

"Kitty-Kitty!"she called to the shy little guy/who ran under a car... Then she saw in his eye--

A curious, wondering, questioning glance/ As he said: "YOU LIKE CATS!" "Can you give me a chance?

He raced to her leg and he rubbied and purried,/Then he purried some MORE, but Roberta was worried!

"Is this somebody's kitty?" she said to Bruce/"He's wandering around out here on the loose!"

Bruce didn't reply. He was already smitten/with the bright-eyed, bright-acting tuxedo kitten!

"Would you folks like a cat?" she asked one of the men./The cat went inside, then got tossed out again!

The junkyard owners wouldn't let him stay/And the closest house looked a mile away...

SO, what do you think the two of them did?/What DO you think the two of them did?

That's RIGHT! In honor of Brucie's SU-BA-RU/He and Roberta have a cat named ROO!

120-mile car ride on Roberta's lap!

We don't think the kitty was ever missed/'cuz Roberta made certain to check CRAIGSLIST!

47

TRULY ROO! by Roberta Gregory

We found Roo at an auto parts junkyard out east of the mountains, late October in the rural far North. (with coyotes!)

He rode home for two hours in my lap. Before we introduced him to Purrrzac we took him to a vet to make sure he didn't have anything "Cat-tagious."

Bruce thought the way he looked into the office window showed he was very bright! Little did we know...

What a SWEETIE!

Unfortunately, he never got along well with Purrrzac!

12 years old with cancer and quite happy to be the only kitty.

About 9 months, slightly psycho and not yet a "Cat-strato."

I unsuccessfully tried to find a new home for him. Efforts to keep the two separated were not easy with three floors and few doors!

"HANG IN THERE, BABY" pose!

Purrrzac in attic room

old ballet poster boards no barrier to determined cat!

He was always perfect with litter box habits, unlike Purrrzac's lifelong quirk of sometimes pooping on the floor!

Why would anyone get rid of such a great cat?

But, one of his main forms of communication seemed to be BITING! (Annoyed? Trying to "tell" us something? No discernible reason?)

Maybe I can GUESS why...

So I hired a pet behavior expert, who studied Roo, and then declared:

He's a Border Collie in a cat suit!

Wow! He's--- THAT bright?

We had to keep him mentally stimulated to prevent his "acting out". fortunately, he can be lots of fun to play with!

Also I think "Tag! You're it!" had to be invented by CATS!

It was far less easy getting him to coexist with Purrrzac. Unfortunately the problem solved itself when her cancer finally caught up with her and she went off to "Kitty heaven."

Roo really IS quite the cat! Never have we felt so aware of being in the presence of a bright little consciousness - an intelligence that just happens to be a different species!

Over the years, he's gotten less "bitey" and more "Lovey!"

And, he's a "Tuxedo!" what IS it that makes them so.. different? Uncanny?

This is his favorite room now!

ROO is one cat in a MILLION! As exasperating as he is enlightening!

♪ Little Cat Roo, Little Cat Roo, ✳ what are we going to DO with you?

Against black background he has a HUMAN profile!

✳ I guess we just appreciate you for simply being - TRULY ROO!

ROO meets... "Mom's" iPad

very bright cat!

"Cat app" with mouse

story: Roberta Gregory

Roo swats at mouse for a while...

changes screen to email...

At this point, "mom" intervenes...

Roo seriously tries to catch mouse...

Cat "pounce-and-pivot"

When mouse goes into "hole" Roo looks under iPad..

When mouse emerges, Roo swats some more..

Roo bites iPad...

..then smacks it HARD with both front paws.

Roo climbs on "moms" dresser and opens top drawer...

..gets out pair of socks rolled together.

Roo goes out to hallway and tosses it like a mouse.

Roo gets bored and leaves.

© 2014 Roberta Gregory

PLAY Kitty

Young Purrrzac was a cuddly crawl-under-the-covers-and-purr-like-mad kitten.

Purr-PURR-PURRR.

Story: Roberta Gregory

But when she grew up, she wasn't a "lap kitty." She still loved being with "her people"... on her own terms, of course.

RESPECTFUL DISTANCE

And at dinnertime, respectful shoulder-skritches are.-- HIGHLY appreciated!

I just HATE eating alone...

But if there's TOO MUCH "touchie." She reacts as if indecent liberties have been forced upon her!

FRESH!

Cats are good at "setting boundaries." But, her lovely, plush fur is SUCH a temptation for heavy petting!

Of course, she usually follows up a swat or warning bite with a reassuring head-bump.

Just because I'm ANGRY...

--Doesn't mean I don't LOVE you!

She did start a ritual of: hopping onto my bed, purring and rubbing and kneading, and then settling next to me.--

Purr. PURR-Purrr PURRR-purrr...--

--for about a minute — THEN dashing off as if she remembers she has something else to do!

A kitty's work is NEVER done!

And later go sleep in my closet.

One day, I read something very interesting in a book I was given.

There are two types of friendly personality in cats— one prefers petting— the other prefers play.

I could have told you THAT...

"IS YOUR CAT CRAZY?" by John C. Wright, 1994

Purrrzac was a PLAY KITTY! I finally caught on that when she scratched the carpet, she was asking us to-- PLAY!

NO.. I'm NOT doing this just to... ANNOY you...

"PLAY" tail!

It makes sense now. I had a kitty who'd scratch the carpet in front of a door she wanted opened.

And another who was PROBABLY trying to get me to play with him by knocking things off the desk! (And THEN giving me a "Look".)

NO! BAD KITTY!

CLUELESS Roberta!

Purrrzac had a playful way of being Bruce's "MUSE" when he worked -- and THEN would push pens off the desk.

Okay-- BREAK TIME!

Any small object that could be swatted or skittered across the floor was a "toy."

But those pastel-colored sponge rubber golf balls were... IT!

She didn't seem to be built for speed-- but... LOOKS can be deceiving!

The WINGS pattern on her shoulders was a giveaway!

Low-slung tail

She DOES look like a RACCOON trundling along!

She'd completely lose any dignity and roll down the carpeted steps in pursuit of her prey...

And her reflexes are astounding! Even though I throw the ball FAST.. ..and her paws are a BLUR.... She'd hit it right BACK to me.. ..well, maybe 80% of the time!

Ball stuck in claw

Try gazing at things upside-down... like a cat! It's a bit like meditation!

And if she MISSES, it's usually my BAD THROW!

QUICKER-THAN-THE-EYE MOVES:

The Flying-Leap Under-paw Flip!

The Biped Catch-and-Toss!

Also catches FLIES this way!

The Tail-Over-Teakettle Tumble-Toss!

And, for reasons of her own, and at odd times, she BRINGS us those sponge rubber balls

I USED to think she brought it to PLAY with...But when I'd toss the ball she looked rather appalled...

Talking with her mouth full!

Rrnt--

mmrf--

Tell-tale damp ball!

They mysteriously appear all over the place, as if by MAGIC!

GET it, girl!

what....?

Maybe it's a mama-cat-and-kitten thing. Maybe it's a GIFT. NOW I let her head-bump my hand and THANK her.

For instance, one of the first times I stayed over with Bruce, in the morning she had left TWO balls in front of the bed!

"Awww..."

"She's never done THAT before!"

Shag carpet

And, SOMETIMES--I realize there's STILL a lot I have yet to learn. Like.. WHY are the three balls in the bathroom all--- BLUE? Just a COINCIDENCE?

"And why are BOTH balls in my room.. --YELLOW?"

As much as we want to try to understand these little beings, there is STILL so much we'll never know.

I WANTED to get her a kitten pal to keep her young.. but Purrrzac had a way of POOPING in strange places, sometimes... AND I didn't want an impressionable young kitty to pick up this bad habit!

"Well... SHE does it!"

Of course, pushing 10, Purrrzac is STILL in touch with her "inner kitten."

Just recently, she trained us to give her newspaper instead of litter to do her "duty" on--- And, she's been pretty good.

"Well... unless my "people"... -are lax in THEIR duties! Tsk! you have to keep on them CONSTANTLY!"

I still feel bad for single kitties.. They can't pass on any of their "Cat Culture" to the others in the household. So, what I CAN do is learn from her and then try to pass it on as best I can!

Head-bump very often means--THANK YOU!

"I LOVE the KITTEN in you!"

What I MOST want to learn is.. There's ALWAYS time to-- PLAY!

The connection with another little soul of a different species--right in one's HOME... is truly a GIFT!

"wow.. what a BRIGHT little consciousness!"

"these humans are --DUMB! What would they DO without me...?"

What's behind those mysterious eyes?

©'10 Roberta Gregory

55

The Cat Came Back

...again!

Story, Roberta Gregory

1999-2012

After two years of Cancer (and doing pretty well) it was time to say goodbye to Purrrzac... at least she got to be at home.

We still had Roo, so we weren't completely catless, but it was still very sad. I'd made the arrangements, so I felt especially "responsible."

> She was... why did I should'v... she was scar... my fault for... why did I...

> READY TO DIE TO THE VET WAITED!

Four days later, we wanted to watch one of our favorite movies: What Dreams May Come. It has to do with death and meeting your loved ones on "the other side."

snf

Midway through it, when dead Robin Williams meets up with his deceased daughter....

> What's THAT?

> I felt a CAT walk behind me.. I really FELT something.

> Roo went upstairs a while ago!

Purrrzac's favorite spot was the pillow at the end of the sofa she'd have to walk behind Bruce to get to.

I haven't "noticed" her since, but I was happy she at least came by to finish watching the movie with us...

A VERY FINE CAT...

...indeed!

by Roberta Gregory

I had to say goodbye to my kitty, Pushkin, on September 9, 2006. He'd had a LOT of health problems...

Poor baby-boy... You're so.. TIRED, aren't you?

Can't hold head up.

..but THIS time, he seemed to be ready to "go"... I HOPE!

I COULD go into more detail about his last days.. but it would make me too sad. And, that's not the point of his story... or of ANYONE'S story, really!

NOBODY gets out ALIVE..

We'll probably ALL have sad endings.

So, instead, I want to tell what a wonderful cat he was. He was VERY smart! And, handsome enough to be a feline movie star!

- Red tabby
- white shirt-front
- WICKEDLY striped tail!

It never showed up in photos, but he had the prettiest-shaped eyes... but only when he was looking at me ..

charming white squiggle on nose!

Maybe only I got to see them.

He liked it when I'd lie down on the carpet near him. He'd yawn and stretch and roll...And I'd imitate him. Then, he'd REPEAT!

Don't forget the TOES..

It felt like he was teaching me... CAT YOGA! Now, after he's gone I still practice his specific stretch.

Like all cats, he had his independent side, but he'd often be close to me. It was like having a friend who happened to be a cat.

Whenever I was working, he'd be snoozing very near by.

At our old home, he'd come and go through an open window and had a bottomless dish of dry cat food.

Just a dream-come-true life for an independent kitty!

But, even so, he'd usually be waiting for me whenever I came home and he'd escort me inside with his tail high.

♫ I've got a cat...
...a very fine ♪
♪ cat, indeed --

"OUR" song!

He was a cat of very sophisticated tastes. If I was eating something, he always expected me to offer him some, to see if it was anything he might like.

Nope.-

Sometimes it WAS...sometimes it WASN'T... but it was always considered polite to offer!

He was built like a muscular little lion, and always seemed to be posing for me. Now I wish I had done more drawings of him.

He had the most active TAIL! When he was outside or considering something, it would thrash and whip and practically go in CIRCLES!

Ooh... what's around the corner?

I wish I'd gotten a video of his TAIL, too...

I read somewhere that when a cat has an active tail, it means it's either very irritated... or -- "Just thinking."

With Pushkin, I have no doubts that it was the LATTER!

When he was asleep, I'd speak to him across the room and his tail would start flicking and swishing in response.

If I came up close and whispered to him, he would start purring in his sleep...

When he was young, he was very friendly and outgoing to the neighborhood cats, but he'd usually get hissed at and swatted in response.

Still, he had a few cat buddies he liked to hang out with: Mit-mat, the tuxedo cat; the blonde kitty down the street, and his sometimes-rival, Wally.

It's PUSHKIN!

MAINTAIN PROPER DISTANCE

The PEOPLE neighbors knew him, too!

Now I wish I'd gotten a kitten for him. He would have made such a wonderful "big brother" cat!

But, by then, he was already racking up the vet bills. I could barely afford to keep HIM!

He was starting to have a lot of medical problems: hemorrhagic cystitis, coccidia and pancreatitis which would probably have been the cause of his feline diabetes.

Medical Supply

Plumbing Supply

Pest Control

My neighborhood also had some industrial pollution, and since cats wash themselves, I wonder if his freedom had been to blame.

59

I had to take him to the vet a lot, and he always hated it. There were DOGS there... and painful & intrusive things got done to him.

Hold still.. I'll TRY not to make this hurt.

whats MOM up to now?

For months, he had to take bad-tasting medicine, and then get insulin shots twice a day for years. He was so good about putting up with all of this!

When the house we lived in got sold, we moved in with Bruce, in his condo in a very busy part of the city.

Don't get USED to this, Baby-boy!

Purrrrr

Lying in the sun

Pushkin would have to be an indoor cat. Besides, now he needed to have a lot of medical supervision.

He wasn't happy about it, but accepted it all with typical feline grace and resignation.

I worried about how he'd get along with Bruce's kitty, Purrzac. As an outdoor kitty, Pushkin would "spray" all over the yard.

This could be a PROBLEM..

So, the FIRST time I caught him backing up to something inside, I yelled...

NO!

I could practically read his MIND!

ALL RIGHT... OKAY.. I...THOUGHT it was...OKAY.. ..OBVIOUSLY NOT..!! sheesh!

And, he never sprayed AGAIN! (At least nothing I ever caught.) SEE? I TOLD you he was smart!

Later on, I'd let him go out for supervised stroll-roll-and-sniff-abouts, near our building, and he was USUALLY pretty good about not trying to run off...

There goes the TAIL!

...though he'd HISS at me when I would bring him back inside.

It really felt like we could communicate with each other even though we belonged to two VERY different species.

Yes? What is it NOW?

I pooped in the litter box and it really SMELLS and I'd like you to scoop it out and FLUSH it ... pleeease?

Cats can be "like us" in many ways... and a wonderful link to the animal kingdom, as well... with a bit of MAGIC and MYSTERY mixed in.

A twitch of the whisker to Louis Wain

Even from the beginning, he seemed to have a very moody side, as well. It's hard to explain, but sometimes I got the feeling he was frustrated with his limitations.

It sounds strange, but there were times I wondered if maybe he had been a HUMAN in a former lifetime, who had to come back as a CAT for some reason.

I KNOW... this sounds utterly and completely... WHACKO...

BUT.. on the chance that it may be TRUE... I want to tell Whoever needs to know that he was a very...
... VERY fine cat!

And, I still miss him!

EPILOGUE

The day after I had Pushkin "Put to sleep", I was still in shock... and hoping I hadn't made a HORRIBLE mistake!

What have I DONE? He was my... KITTY! My little CAT FRIEND! He LOVED me.. He TRUSTED me.. And... and... I KILLED him!

Bruce had one of his arts potlucks that evening. Pushkin had always liked to mingle with the guests. Purrzac was much more standoffish..

I should have brought him home. Maybe I could have nursed him back to health.. I could have gotten the vet to make a house call so he could have died in familiar surroundings. or--

I'm so sorry about Pushkin. I'll miss him.

I was sitting by myself and I felt a cat rub against my leg.

That last shot HURT him... That'll be his LAST MEMORY of me... something that... HURT!

OH... Hi, Purrz..

But, Purrzac was sitting up on the STAIRS!

... ACK!

If this WAS Pushkin, it would be the only time I ever "felt" him... posthumously.

One person said there ARE "cat ghosts" and that we may sense his presence around the house—

Now, I LAUGH at doors!

Lookit Purrzac being crazy.. --AGAIN!

A second person told me "cat ghosts" stop by to say farewell, and then they go.

I hope the second person is right. If ever anyone deserved to be free, it's PUSHKIN!

Off on his next big adventure!

©2007 Roberta Gregory

62

CATching Up with Pushkin

©2005
Roberta
Gregory

In Summer, 2003, I had to move into an urban condo... and, my independent kitty, Pushkin, was going to move INDOORS!

Enjoy your yard while you CAN...

THIS is the LIFE!

I knew it would be for the best, but I still felt bad for him...

He loved his little yard and interesting neighborhood.... but he'd developed serious health problems, too... Including pancreatitis.

My previous kitty, Muffy, had gotten pretty sick there, too. The new place was nice and clean... but VERY enclosed.

Medical Supply Warehouse

PLUMBING SUPPLY Co.

Former PEST CONTROL

VROOM!

YOUNG Pushkin-

HONK!

He first showed up in this busy neighborhood! I wouldn't DREAM of letting him out into it NOW!

I think a lot of old (mostly) industrial pollution in the area may have been to. blame.

The large windows looked out onto a very busy street! NOT a safe neighborhood for cats!

The first few days in his new home, Pushkin would go to the door to be let out and I'd say "NO." He would always be a very good sport about it....

But, the day came when I said "NO" again, and I could see the LOOK in his eyes and the droop in his tail...

Fine... BE that way...

I didn't want to go out ANYHOW!

WAIT... you're not... EVER going to let me out.. HUH?

He's just THAT sort of cat. Plus, there were three floors of new home to explore and another kitty to get acquainted with ...

This was the day I DREADED! How do you convince a kitty who's always been "his own person" that this is for his own GOOD?

I tried to cheer him up, but he seemed very sad after that. The traffic outside the big windows scared him, but there was a small one he'd sit at.

Of course, he was always a bit moody, too. His vets called him a "drama queen."

He kept getting sick. He got hemorrhagic cystitis, AND had to have a bad-tasting powder mixed into his food for 6 months to cure his bloody diarrhea... And he still seems to have pancreatitis...

I really began to worry when I saw him drinking a lot of water and peeing a lot...and looking even MORE sad and tired!

He was diagnosed with feline Diabetes. He needs insulin shots twice a day, now... but that's NOT as bad as it sounds.

There is a great Feline Diabetes (.com) web site with lots of wonderful and encouraging folks on their Message Board!

The REALLY hard part is testing his blood sugar. It's pricey to do it at the vet...and even THEY have trouble, with all his biting and scratching!

So far, we have not had much luck testing him at home...

Poor Pushkin! His "Mommy" keeps poking him and giving him icky medicine, and sometimes he STILL doesn't seem to feel very well!

He's such a wonderful, bright kitty. I really wonder what he thinks about all this!

I guess it also helps that he seems to be very forgiving, and, by nature, a happy cat... Whenever he's sound asleep, I come up quietly and whisper...

And he ALWAYS purrs in his sleep!

Bye-Bye MUFFY

I had to have my sweet little kitty, Muffy, put to sleep on December 14..

I hoped she was ready to go. Its so hard to say. She'd been looking miserable for the last few days...

I could tell her stomach really hurt and she couldn't eat anything...

She'd been suffering from an inflammatory bowel for well over a year... She'd projectile-vomit really foul-smelling liquid...

Usually around 2 AM or so!

I would treat her with medicine that she really hated. A lot of the time she'd get better for awhile.

When she felt like eating, I would boil chicken for her. She liked sitting in the kitchen watching it cook.

But after awhile she had more downs than ups. I would offer her a treat and she would just turn her head away, looking really sad.

It was so heartbreaking to see the look on her face.

She came into my life eleven years ago. She literally showed up at my door!

She had to climb a flight of stairs to get to it!

She would NOT take "No" for an answer!

I had another kitty who was very old and in failing health. She was not long for this world...

Her daddy, Cokie, had died earlier and she was on her way to join him.

About the time she died, I finally decided the little black-and-white kitty really did want to live here.

I took her to the vet to see if she needed to be spayed and found out she was pregnant! So, she had an abortion, too.

I got a kitten for BOTH of us. A VERY frisky little guy I called "Jonny-Cat"... (like the one on The kitty-litter package!)

Here's your NEW FRIEND!

Hiss!

Muffy didn't like Jonny-Cat very much. He got VERY sick with diarrhea and nearly died, but I nursed him back to health...

My tummy hurts!

SPLOOT!

No matter HOW sick he was, he'd use the litter box!

Once he got better, I was VERY attached to him. He was REAL smart... and VERY destructive!

STEREO SPEAKER

BICYCLE TIRE

GNAW!

STUFFED ALPACA

AND, he could get into any cupboard in the house. He was more like a monkey than a kitten! I LOVED him!

You SILLY Kitty!

CHEWED SWEATER

They moved to Seattle with me, but Jonny disappeared when I was away at the San Diego comic con!

LOST CAT
CUTE!
Red collar
842

To be honest, I sorta wished Muffy would have been the one to go, but she was the real homebody of the two...

FINALLY... Some peace and QUIET!

Purr...

I kept hoping Jonny might come back, so I never got another cat, which seemed to suit Muffy just fine!

When Jonny comes marching home again...

Give it UP, Girl!

Eventually, I began to appreciate Muffy's more ordinary charms...

Oh, well... I have a NICE kitty...

BORING, but nice!

Actually, she WAS pretty interesting — it took me a while to realize she was meowing NOT because she was HUNGRY, but she wanted me to PLAY with her!

I'M BORED, Mommy!

She'd chase a toy across the floor, then bounce off her "carpet-covered-kitty-condo"! (on PURPOSE!)

Eat CLAW, Mousie!

BOING!

It always made me laugh!

Her FAVORITE game was "kitty-catch". I'd skitter kibbles across the kitchen floor and she'd catch them!

She liked it when I'd SURPRISE her... toss 'em in the air so they'd land BEHIND her and skitter away!

AND, if one landed under the kitchen table, her rules said she HAD to perch on the rungs and reach DOWN for it!

She was also a MAGIC cat! If I put a collar on her, especially a flea collar, it would ALWAYS be gone the next day!

I wished EVERYONE could know what a cool kitty I had, but she was VERY shy of other people!

If people were lucky, they'd get a glimpse of her hiding just outside my bedroom window...

SOMETIMES she'd warm up to someone, especially if she could tell they were a cat lover... or if she saw them enough times...

She WANTED to be friendly but she was SO scared!

She didn't like OTHER cats, either... and there were a LOT of cats in my neighborhood!

On nice days, I'd get my lunch/coffee/newspaper/whatever/and my backrest and call her...

She loved to sit outside with me in our tiny back yard. Since there were two of us, the other cats left her alone!

My basement apartment (and the house next door) had little inset windows that made PERFECT cat perches!

One of her favorite spots inside was the top (empty) box of a pile of boxes that separated my studio from the REST of the room!

I never sat around enough to provide a proper lap.. unless I was sitting at my computer. Then she'd smile up very lovingly at me..

She never got too old to want to play. And I never had to buy expensive cat toys.

She'd have just as much fun with wadded paper or STRING!

Best of all were those little plastic pour-spout inserts from vinegar or soy sauce bottles...

I GOT somethin' for you!

ME?

When they'd roll on the floor, they'd careen around in crazy loops!

SWAT!

She used to like catnip, too, but once, I gave her some of the real STRONG stuff—little flowering tops I got at the farmer's market.

WOW-EEE!

She got so crazed, she thrashed around with one of her little toy mice and accidentally banged her head against the wall!

BONK!

After THAT, she didn't like catnip anymore. Poor Muffy... one thing after another!

Nah... gives me a HEADACHE!

She'd look me right in the eye and "Meow" like she wanted SO much for me to understand her...

Mee-OW!

BOY, is she STUPID!

I read somewhere that cats only say "Me-ow" when they're communicating with people!

Her "I want to go OUT!" meow was different from her "I'm hungry" meow... And she'd usually jump up on a table for emphasis. So, I made SOME progress!

Here!

WOW! WE'RE COMMUNICATING!

MEOW!

She had a charming way of holding up one paw when she was feeling a little shy ...or when she wanted something.

I CAN'T go outside with you right now! I have to WORK!

Are you... SURE?

She KNEW it looked cute!

AND she'd sit with her head tilted back, especially if she wanted some extra food... It MAY sound as though I'm just making this all up...

Ple-e-ase?

works every time...

Tail curled around feet

...but remember, a kitty's CAREER is getting us to do things!

And, for SOME reason, we really don't seem to mind having our strings pulled by them...

Oh, OKAY... I GUESS I can sit here just a... LITTLE longer!

SUCK-ER!

.....DO we?

We DID have ONE big issue... When I was at my drawing table, I had a perfectly good lap going to WASTE....

uhhh...

Now, HOLD still...

So I got a pillow and made her FAVORITE bed!

She always seemed so hurt whenever I went away for a few days... or a few weeks. I'd tell her about it a few days before...

I... THINK it helped!

I waited until the last minute to pack... when she saw my bags she'd go off and sulk!

But, she was always VERY happy to see me when I got back...and didn't do that pouty "attitude" thing like some OTHER cats do!

It's kind of a cliché, but she either thought she was a PERSON... or that I was a rather dysfunctional CAT!

Then she started getting sick... and I started acting WEIRD...and started doing TERRIBLE things to her!

And. when she felt WORSE, then I'D get worse, too! I'd make her eat NASTY tasting stuff...up to 4 times a day!

She NEVER took her pills without a BIG fight!

Even hiding in her safe box didn't help! I'd give her the medicine THERE, or WORSE, pull her OUT of it!

This seemed to violate ANOTHER one of her rules!

And, worst of ALL. I'd keep taking her to the VET!

Later. she got VERY withdrawn. I hoped it was because of the disease and not because she'd stopped forgiving me for doing all these terrible things.

But animals don't know how to give UP, so you have to decide for them... but it's HARD.

Especially for CATS, who seem to have their own agenda!

And I was the only person she ever really trusted.

First time in 25 years I haven't had a cat. I don't know when I'll get another.

Thank You's

A huge "Thank You" to those of you who have shared your cat stories with me, the ones I have illustrated for this volume, and the ones that I will draw in the near future, and to those who may have fallen through the cracks as I misplaced email addresses over the years. (Please get back in touch with me.) Also, thank you, contributors, for your patience, observational skills and your love and compassion for the feline members of your family. We still have so much to learn about the wonderfully interconnected network of life forms sharing this world with us, but a cat in the home is a fine place to start. A big "Thank You" to Donna Barr for knowing a lot more than I do about the techie details of putting a book together, and for that gorgeous color job on the cover. Interestingly enough, she has published her own true tales drawn book collection, *A Little Death.* A very general "Thank You" to all of you friends and colleagues who have been so encouraging and enthusiastic about this project, despite the length of time it took to finally get it together. Thank you to Bruce Taylor for being such a good kitty co-parent with me. And, Thank you to cats, everywhere for your efforts to get through to us humans. Don't give up; we'll catch on eventually.

And, a big "Thank You" in advance to those of you who are now eager to share your own stories. I would love to do at least one more of these books, so I have pages to fill. Contact information is in the front of the book or on the True Cat Toons website.

Roberta Gregory has been writing and drawing her own unique stories for a very long time. Her early work in print dates back to the early 1970s and she published her first comic book, *Dynamite Damsels*, in 1976. She is considered a pioneer of women's independent comics. Her stories appeared in many underground comic anthologies such as *Wimmen's Comix* and *Gay Comix* and she published two more books, *Winging It* and *Sheila and the Unicorn*, in the late 1980s. During the 1990s, Roberta became well known for the 40 issues and several collections of her *Naughty Bits* comic book, published by Fantagraphics, for which she received several Eisner nominations. Its notorious Bitchy Bitch character starred in a weekly comic strip, three stage productions and a cable television animated series in the early 2000s. Roberta published her collection of travel comics, *Follow Your Art* in 2010, and she has many other projects in the works, but she is happy to finally see the first collection of True Cat Toons in print. She continues to create the sorts of stories she would like to read, and will be doing so for the foreseeable future. You can keep up with everything else she is up to at robertagregory.com